A Ch.. ... ...
the Principal

by Rachel Johns
illustrated by Jeesoo Lee

SCHOOL PUBLISHERS

Printed in China

ISBN 10: 0-15-350658-X
ISBN 13: 978-0-15-350658-1

Ordering Options
ISBN 10: 0-15-350599-0 (Grade 2 On-Level Collection)
ISBN 13: 978-0-15-350599-7 (Grade 2 On-Level Collection)
ISBN 10: 0-15-357839-4 (package of 5)
ISBN 13: 978-0-15-357839-7 (package of 5)

4 5 6 7 8 9 10   985   15 14 13 12 11 10 09 08

Characters

Teacher

Mrs. North

Pedro

Sarah

Carmel

Setting: In the principal's office at a town school

Teacher: Good morning, Mrs. North. Three of my students would like to ask you some questions.

Mrs. North: Of course. What would you like to know?

Pedro: We want to ask you about the new playground.

Sarah: Then we will report back to our classmates.

4

Mrs. North: Who is going to start?

Carmel: I will. Why are you building a new playground at our school?

Mrs. North: The old playground is not big enough. The new playground will have better equipment. I hope it will be the best in the area.

Pedro: How did you decide what the playground should have?

Mrs. North: I must admit that it was extremely difficult.

Teacher: That's true.

Mrs. North: A group of teachers exchanged ideas with students and their parents. We asked them to draw plans of what they would like the playground to look like. Many plans were delivered to my office.

Pedro: What were the plans like?

Mrs. North: They were great. People had thought about the playground carefully. We had to choose the best playground we could to serve the school community.

Sarah: What do you mean to serve the school community?

Mrs. North: A lot of children attend this school. We want them and their families to be able to use the playground after school and on weekends.

Pedro: Are you building everything the parents and children asked for?

Mrs. North: We were very serious about building what parents and children wanted. However, it wouldn't have been feasible to build everything they wanted. People have different personalities and want different things.

Teacher: We think the new playground will have something for everyone.

Carmel: What will the playground have?

Mrs. North: It will have swings and a slide. There will also be a sandbox and a basketball court.

Sarah: That sounds great. I love basketball!

Mrs. North: If you get tired of playing, there will be an area with comfortable benches where you can sit and rest.

Carmel: We might need a rest after all that playing!

Mrs. North: There will also be lots of trees that will provide shade on sunny days.

Pedro: When will the playground be finished?

Mrs. North: It will open on the fourth of May. Of course, that's if the builders accomplish the job on time!

Sarah: Do you have any plans for the opening?

Mrs. North: Yes. We have invited a special guest to open the playground.

Carmel: We heard that the special guest is the mayor. Is this true?

Mrs. North: Yes, it is.

Teacher: We will have a big crowd if the mayor comes.

12

Teacher: Mrs. North, thank you for answering the questions.

Sarah: We are looking forward to telling our classmates about the new playground.

Pedro: Everyone will be very excited.

13

Mrs. North: The school can be proud of the new playground.

Children: We can't wait for it to open!

Think Critically

1. What are two words that you would use to tell about Mrs. North?

2. What was going to be on the new playground?

3. Read page 8 again. What do you think the word *feasible* means?

4. Why did the school need a new playground?

5. Would you like to play on the new playground? Why or why not?

 **Social Studies**

Write a Paragraph The story took place in a school. Write a paragraph telling how your school today is different from schools long ago.

School-Home Connection Talk about *A Chat with the Principal* with a family member. Then talk about places where you like to play.

Word Count: 500